POLYCHORAL MOTETS

Recent Researches in the Music of the Renaissance is one of four quarterly series (Middle Ages and Early Renaissance; Renaissance; Baroque Era; Pre-Classical, Classical, and Early Romantic Eras) which make public the early music that is being brought to light in the course of current musicological research.

Each volume is devoted to works by a single composer or in a single genre of composition, chosen because of their potential interest to scholars and performers, and prepared for publication according to the standards that govern the making of all reliable historical editions.

Subscribers to this series, as well as patrons of subscribing institutions, are invited to apply for information about the "Copyright-Sharing Policy" of A-R Editions, Inc., under which the contents of this volume may be reproduced free of charge for performance use.

Correspondence should be addressed:

A-R Editions, Inc.
152 West Johnson Street
Madison, Wisconsin 53703

RECENT RESEARCHES IN THE MUSIC OF THE RENAISSANCE • VOLUME XVIII

Hieronymus Praetorius

POLYCHORAL MOTETS

Part I: Six Motets for Two Choirs

Edited by Frederick K. Gable

A-R EDITIONS, INC. • MADISON

Contents

Part I

Preface

The Composer and His Works

The Praetorius family of Hamburg—not related, so far as is known, with the family of Michael Praetorius, Hieronymus's more famous contemporary—produced a succession of organists and composers who served the large churches of that city for over a century.[1] Jacob Praetorius (d. 1586) began the family tradition in 1558, when he assumed the post of chief organist at the Jakobikirche. Jacob's son Hieronymus, born August 10, 1560, received his earliest instruction at the organ from his father, and later studied music in Cologne supported partly by a stipend from his father's church. In 1582 Hieronymus abandoned the position at Erfurt he had assumed in 1580 to return to Hamburg as assistant organist under his father. When Jacob Praetorius died in 1586, Hieronymus succeeded him as chief organist at the Jakobikirche and held the position until his own death, January 27, 1629. Two of Hieronymus's sons carried the family name to other large Hamburg churches: Jacob II (1586-1651), who studied under Sweelinck, served Petrikirche after 1603; Johannes, also a pupil of Sweelinck, was organist at Nicolaikirche from 1616 until his death in 1661. Thus, from 1560 to 1661 at least one Praetorius held the post of organist in a major church in Hamburg, and between 1616 and 1629 three of the city's four principal churches were served by members of the Praetorius family.

In the judgment of present-day scholars, Hieronymus Praetorius is by far the most distinguished representative of his lineage, noteworthy for his sacred vocal works in the "German-Venetian" style of polychoral composition, a judicious blending of late-Renaissance and early-Baroque usages into a form that is both musically coherent and artistically persuasive. The style of writing for divided choirs which had been developed at Venice, principally by Andrea and Giovanni Gabrieli, was slow to spread to Germany; only two genuinely polychoral works—Johann Walter's *Holdseliger meins Herzen Trost* (1566)[2] and Leonhart Schröter's *Herr Gott dich loben wir* (1571, printed in 1576)[3]—seem to have appeared in sixteenth-century Germany before the publication of Hans Leo Hassler's earliest polychoral works in Lindner's *Continuatio cantionum sacrarum* of 1588. Hassler may be considered to have inaugurated the polychoral trend in Germany; during the two decades following Lindner's publication, composers such as Blasius Amon (1590), Gregor Aichinger (1590), Philippus Dulichius (1590), Andreas Raselius (1595), Hieronymus Praetorius (1599), Georg Poss (1599), Christian Erbach (1600), Adam Gumpelzhaimer (1601), Daniel Lagkner (1602), Friedrich Weissensee (1602), Michael Praetorius (1605), and Christoph Demantius (1609) published their own initial works for divided choirs, followed by Schein (1615), Schütz (1619), and Scheidt (1620).

Although the pupils of Andrea and Giovanni Gabrieli settled only in south Germany and Austria, developing there the polychoral style they had learned at Venice, most of the later *concertato* compositions which grew out of precisely that same Venetian polychoral style were written in *northern* Germany, where the influence of the Gabrielis and of Hassler was weaker. The wide circulation of vocal collections such as Lindner's *Sacrae cantiones* (1585), Victorinus's *Thesaurus Litanarium* (1596), and Kaspar Hassler's *Sacrae symphoniae* (1598) may have influenced the composers of north Germany to experiment with the German-Venetian style; the polychoral works of Jacob Handl (1580, 1586, 1587, 1591) were well-known in most large European cities; the Counter-Reformation activities of the Jesuits throughout northern Germany included the promotion of polychoral music by Palestrina, the Gabrielis, and Victoria; and, perhaps most significantly, an *Orgelprobe* held at Gröningen in 1596 brought together, among others, Kaspar Hassler, Hans Leo Hassler, Michael Praetorius, and Hieronymus Praetorius,[4] out of whose meeting may have proceeded the two Praetoriuses' inspiration to begin the composition of polychoral works.

In any case, the available evidence shows clearly that Philippus Dulichius and Hieronymus Praetorius were the earliest north-German composers to adopt the polychoral style without any prior exposure to Venice. The special influence exerted by Hieronymus Praetorius on his own generation of musicians is attested by the publication of his collected works in five volumes between 1616 and 1625 as well as by the frequent appearance of his works in popular collections; thus, as the principle pioneer of polychoral writing in north Germany, Praetorius surely deserves recognition as the major forerunner, if not as the direct ancestor, of the *concertato* style of church-composition that flourished so splendidly in north Germany during the Baroque era.

The vocal works of Hieronymus Praetorius began to appear in 1599 and had achieved print in their final form by 1625. Of the five volumes in the remarkable *opera omnia* project—only one published work, a parody mass, *Missa Ascendo ad patrem meum* for six voices in Vintzius, *Missae ad praecipuos* (Erfurt, 1630), does not appear in it—Volume I appeared in two preliminary editions, 1599 and 1607, and in a third, "finished" edition, 1622; each edition added more motets. Volume II appeared in 1602 and again in 1622, with an added Magnificat setting. Volumes III-V were published as "finished" editions in 1616, 1618, and 1625, respectively.[5] The five volumes contain 101 motets for five to twenty voices (six motets with German text, the rest with Latin text); nine eight-voice Magnificats (one in each of the eight ecclesiastical modes with an additional setting in the fifth mode, all nine Magnificats presenting only the even-numbered verses of the text in polyphany); six parody Masses for five to eight voices (two of the Masses based on motets by Jacob Meiland and Stephan Felis, the remainder on Praetorius's own motets); and three motets by Jacob Praetorius II.[6] There are no known surviving autographs of Praetorius's vocal works.[7]

Motets by Praetorius appear in printed collections of the early seventeenth century compiled or published by Bodenschatz (1603[1], 1618[1], 1621[2]), Phalèse (1609[1]), Schadaeus (1613[2]), Petraeus (1640[1]), and Profius (1642[4]).[8] Twenty-one vocal chorale settings by Praetorius are included in *Die Melodeyen Gesangbuch* (Hamburg, 1604), and 39 excerpts from his works appear in Erasmus Sartorius's *Institutionum musicarum tractatio nova et brevis* (Hamburg, 1635). The only known instrumental works by Praetorius are eight Magnificats for organ, one in each of the ecclesiastical modes, probably written for performance in alternation with plainsong; they are not, however, musically related to the nine vocal Magnificats.[9]

The Polychoral Motets

The polychoral motets of Hieronymus Praetorius, quite apart from their historical importance, are the product of a distinctive, mature, and engaging musical personality. In many ways the motets bear a close resemblance to those of Hassler and Lasso, although Praetorius's writing is less polyphonic and more harmonic than Lasso's, and is considerably less structured and more varied than Hassler's.

Looking further afield for comparisons, one finds that Praetorius's polychoral motets are much more contrapuntal than Handl's; more inclined to vivid textual expression and free treatment of dissonance than Palestrina's; less given to the use of the German chorale, independent instrumental parts, and solo singing with obligatory continuo than Michael Praetorius's; more restrained in textual expression and more vocal in style than the late polychoral motets of Giovanni Gabrieli.

In contrast with many polychoral works of the late sixteenth and early seventeenth centuries, Praetorius's motets avoid the simple exchange of chordal statements among choirs by the frequent introduction of imitative writing, by the maintenance of a steady flow of short rhythmic values, and by the use of "broken homophony"—the preservation of a distinguishable homophonic movement within which the individual voice-parts are allowed a certain independence by the use of varied rhythms, interpolated rests, disjunct statements of text, syncopation, and short motivic imitations. The quasi-polyphonic result is combined variously with chordal and imitative writing to produce the characteristic style of Praetorius's polychoral motets. Praetorius's frequently disjunct and angular part-writing, in which the composer does not hesitate to use leaps of a tritone as well as diminished and augmented fourths and fifths, and sevenths, suggests that the vocal parts are fitted to a harmonic scheme rather than conceived as independent melodic lines—an impression that is particularly noticeable when a single voice-part is sounded independently. Nonetheless, the fusion of all parts in Praetorius's "broken homophonic" style creates a rich sonority, musically satisfying and often exciting. Abstract contrapuntal devices such as canon, diminution, augmentation, and invertible counterpoint rarely appear in Praetorius's works, and the common Renaissance *cantus-firmus* technique is entirely absent from them.

Harmonically, Praetorius's motets fall between modality and tonality, by virtue of the mixture of root-movement in fourths and fifths with movement in thirds and seconds. Inversions of triads rarely occur on strong beats (a typical use of inversions appears in measures 26-27 of *Angelus ad pastores ait*). Modulations appear only occasionally, in passing or at cadences. Accidentals transforming the modes into clear major or minor scales appear frequently, although melodic chromaticism is restricted to harmonic contexts of root progressions by a third. Dissonant strong-beat passing tones and mild cross-relations occur occasionally, most often at cadences (see, for example, measure 32 of *Dixit Dominus*, measures 4-5 of *Angelus ad pastores ait*, measures 62-63 of *Nunc dimittis*, and measure 14 of *Laudate Dominum*). Praetorius anticipates Baroque practice in the frequent reduction of the common Renaissance suspension-cadence pattern to half its normal time-span. A common trait of Praetorius's harmonic writing is the close juxtaposition of major and minor versions of a triad, often employed for a clearly discernible expressive effect.

Praetorius's handling of multiple choruses reflects no radical departure from the common practice of his contemporaries, but reveals, rather, an imaginative use of alternating *tutti* and antiphonal passages. The composer avoids, for the most part, the simple exchange of identical musical statements between choruses, choosing rather to alter responding statements by a change of pitch level, an exchange of voice parts, an embellishment or reworking of the initial statement, or the recomposition of certain voice parts within the responding chorus while the initial statement is preserved in the remaining voices; Praetorius's setting of nine repetitions of the text "quia viderunt oculi mei," measures 37-61 of *Nunc dimittis*, vividly illustrates his expert use of varied alternation between choruses. Overlapping choral statements are commonly used to sustain the forward movement of a motet and to prevent the impression of over-sectionalization. Half-measure overlap is Praetorius's usual practice, although shorter and longer overlaps appear from time to time; lengthy overlapping almost to the extent of canon appears in *Ein Kindelein so löbelich*, measures 89-95 and elsewhere. In motets for three or four choruses, two choruses are occasionally joined in one large chorus, contrasting with the remaining voices. Usually a voice part sounds only with its own chorus, but there are exceptions to the general rule: a single voice from one chorus sings with the opposite chorus in *Ecce Dominus veniet*, measures 88-92, in *Ein Kindelein so löbelich*, measures 13-15 and 60-61, and in *Nunc dimittis*, measures 37-38 and 43-46. The full sonority of the combined choirs is often used to create a broad, majestic final cadence, to conclude subsections of a motet, or to emphasize the sense of such textual passages as "with the whole heart," "all the nations," and "all the earth."

To vary the vocal texture of his music, Praetorius often employs choruses of contrasting range (see, for example, *Cantate Domino*, *Ecce quam bonum*, *Dixit Dominus*, *Jubilate Deo*, and *Domine probasti me* in the present edition); in two of his motets he achieves a singular vocal texture by sounding a voice part consistently an octave or more away from the other voices in its chorus (see the Tenor of Chorus I in *Ecce quam bonum* and the Cantus of Chorus III in *Angelus ad pastores ait*). The benign mood of the texts to *Ein Kindelein so löbelich* and *Tota pulchra es* is matched by the texture of the music, restricted to comparatively high-ranging voices. Thus, Praetorius makes good use of the total range of pitches available to him in his polychoral writing, spanning the four octaves from contra *B-flat* to two-line *B-flat*; indeed, *Domine probasti me* nearly exhausts the entire range. Marshalling eight to twenty voices within this expansive range, Praetorius is able to maintain a standard triadic disposition of two roots, one fifth, and one third in four-part writing, with more roots and more fifths added as the number of voices increases (although the single third is common to all numbers of voices). Since Praetorius often has a very large number of parts sounding together, he accomplishes a remarkable feat in maintaining his standard disposition without awkward voice-leading, abnormally expansive part-ranges, and frequent unison-doubling.

Praetorius's musical evocation of his texts is subtle, reserved, and rarely ostentatious; the composer seems to follow the rule that although text should never be allowed to overwhelm musical considerations, the music itself can be strengthened by frequent touches of text expression. Praetorius's settings of text are predominantly syllabic, but his music does include melismatic passages to emphasize important words or to sustain sequential patterns (see, for example, measures 36-39 of *Cantate Domino*). The rhythmic animation and strongly accentuated text declamation which are prominent stylistic features of Praetorius's writing—created by contrasting rhythmic patterns, syncopations (sometimes of five quarter-notes' duration), imitation at eighth-note intervals, and shifts of accentuation from an established pattern—are often used precisely to intensify textual expression, as in *Angelus ad pastores ait*, measures 12-14, 16-18, and 20-23, where "gaudium magnum" ("great joy") is set to shorter note-values than the preceding text.

The structure of Praetorius's motets is determined, in conventional fashion, by the phrase-by-phrase presentation of the text, but Praetorius manages to modify or extend his motets by the repetition of musical sections, occasionally unchanged but usually subjected to considerable variation. Thus, although *Angelus ad pastores ait* is composed almost entirely of literally repeated sections, *Tota pulchra es* presents an imaginative example of varied repetition in presenting music from measures 1-2 as the imitative material in measures 73-81, after which the motet concludes with the conventional repetition of six-measure and four-measure sections appearing earlier in the piece. A still more subtle and extensive use of varied repetition is combined with a triple-meter refrain in *Cantate Domino*, giving the work a large measure of structural coherence and unity that is quite independent of the text. In *Ein Kindelein so löbelich*, one of his few motets based on a German chorale melody, all the phrases of the original melody appear in either the Cantus or Bassus parts at least once, set either in imitative or in homophonic style; a partial setting of the German carol *Joseph lieber, Joseph mein*, interrupted by two duple measures of vocal fanfare, concludes this joyous Christmas motet.

In sum, the polychoral motets of Hieronymus Praetorius may be said to represent a successful moderation of Renaissance tradition and Baroque innovation, blending the characteristic elements of the old and the new styles into an internally consistent medium of artistic expression.

The Performance of the Motets

The late-Renaissance practice of using instruments either to double the vocal parts of a motet or to replace them altogether is definitely applicable to the polychoral motets of Praetorius; in most cases, in fact, the commingling of voices and instruments is preferable to a purely vocal performance because the mixture enhances the grand sonorities that were clearly intended by the composer.

Fortunately for modern performers, the *Rechnungsbuch* of St. Gertrude's Chapel in Hamburg preserves a detailed account of the presentation of one of Hieronymus Praetorius's polychoral motets during the composer's lifetime.[10] For the dedication service at St. Gertrude's in 1607, five polychoral motets were performed; one of the five, Praetorius's *Herr Gott dich loben wir*,[11] employed singers alone in the first chorus, cornetts and sackbuts for the second chorus, viols and a regal for the third, and solo organ for the fourth. The account does not specify how singers were distributed in the choruses other than the first. This information, together with what is generally known about performance practice in the late Renaissance and the early Baroque, clearly supports the principle that modern performers are free to exercise considerable imagination in mixing or doubling voices and instruments in any of the motets in the present edition. With proper attention to the balancing and blending of voices and instruments, one may legitimately use recorders, viols, wooden transverse flutes, krummhorns, sorduns, dulcians, racketts, cornetts, sackbuts, lutes, harpsichords, regals, organs, and possibly even violins in the performance of Praetorius's music; the organ alone may be substituted for an entire chorus, or may play continuously throughout a motet from a *basso seguente* part which could easily be prepared from this edition if it were considered necessary.

Musical factors intrinsic to the motets should, of course, be allowed to temper the performer's decision whether to assign any given part to voices, instruments, or a combination of the two. In *Angelus ad pastores ait*, for example, the plainsong phrases definitely must be sung; in *Ecce quam bonum* and *Laudate Dominum* the division of the text between choruses suggests that some voices should be used in each chorus to provide for a complete presentation of the text. Choruses whose parts lie within the normal range and agility of the human voice—the second chorus of *Domine probasti me*, for example—should probably be performed either by voices alone or by an appropriate combination of voices and instruments. On the other hand, some of the motets in this edition contain parts which seem better suited to instrumental than to vocal performance, by virtue of their unusually disjunct nature, their unusually low range, or their heavily ornamented melodic style; examples are the Altus part of Chorus I and the second Tenor part of Chorus II in *Ecce quam bonum*, and the first and second Cantus parts of Chorus I in *Cantate Domino*. Performance of certain motets entirely by instruments is not at all out of the question; the rhythmic nature of *Laudate Dominum* and *Jubilate Deo*, for example, suggests that both pieces could be effectively presented by an exclusively instrumental ensemble.

The embellishment of vocal lines in Praetorius's motets is both historically correct and musically effective, although, since Praetorius's musical texture is often thick and rhythmically active just as it is notated, any attempt at embellishment should be undertaken cautiously, restricted, perhaps, to the use of trills and turns at cadences, the addition of diatonic passing-tones, and the judicious variation of melodic lines in repetition. Adventurous performers may wish to work out more elaborate embellishment, using such sixteenth-century treatises as those by Silvestro Ganassi, Hermann Finck, Francesco Rogniono, and

Girolamo dalla Casa, as well as the enlightening examples presented in Ferand's *Improvisation in Nine Centuries of Western Music*.[12]

Questions concerning tempo and dynamics must be settled according to the judgment of the individual conductor: Praetorius offers no cues to the dynamic realization of his music, and his mensuration signs are used so haphazardly that one can draw no reliable conclusions from them in establishing the "correct" tempo of any given piece. On the basis of my experience I would suggest a tempo of ♩=70-80 M.M.

The Edition

The present two-volume edition increases from seven to eighteen (out of a total of 51) the number of polychoral motets by Hieronymus Praetorius available in published modern editions as of this writing.[13] I have transcribed the music from microfilm copies of printed part-books and a manuscript Bassus part-book of the "final" editions of Volumes I, II, IV, and V of Praetorius's collected vocal works, located in the Stifts- och Läroverksbiblioteket in Västeras, Sweden; a few pages missing from the Västeras holdings were supplied by the Royal College of Music and the British Museum, London.

The part-books for Praetorius's collected vocal works bear the designations Cantus, Altus, Tenor, Bassus, Quinta vox, Sexta vox, Septima vox, and Octava vox; the additional voices for motets in more than eight parts are appended to one or another of the standard part-books. The collected-works edition also includes a "basso continuo" part which is in fact merely a *basso seguente*, presenting the lowest-sounding note at any given point in the music; since this *basso seguente* is musically extrinsic to Praetorius's compositions themselves, and does not appear in the earlier editions of Volumes I and II of the collected works, I have decided against encumbering the present edition with it.

The tenor part-books of Praetorius's collected works consistently yield the most complete information about the publication; the title pages of the tenor part-books for Volumes I, II, IV, and V, respectively, read as follows in the "final" published edition:

CANTIONES SACRAE / DE / FESTIS PRAECI- / PUIS TOTIUS AN- / NI V: VI. VII. IIX. X. XII. / VOCUM: / Quae sunt / OPERUM MUSICORUM / Tomus Primus / Divinae majestatis honori / Reipublicae Christianae & Musicae / BONO / Concinnatus & Dedicatus / Denuo ab ipso autore correctus, Motectis aliquot auctus, & in / gratiam Musicae peri-torum BASSO CONTINUO / exornatus / Ab / HIERONYMO PRAETORIO Sen. / Organista ad D. Jacobi / TENOR. / HAMBURGI, / Ex Officina Typographica PAULI LANGI / Sumptibus autoris / ANNO M. DC. XXII.

CANTICUM B. MARIAE / VIRGINIS. / SEU / MAGNIFICAT / OCTO VOCUM. / Super Octo Tonos Consuetos / QUOD EST / OPERUM MUSICORUM / Tomus Secundus / Divinae majestatis honori / Reipublicae Christianae & Musicae / BONO / Concinnatus & dedicatus / Denuo ab ipso autore correctus, Motectis aliquot 8. 10. & 12. Vocum / auctus & in gratiam Musicae peritorum BASSO CONTINUO / exornatus / ab / HIERONYMO PRAETORIO Sen. / Organista ad D. Jacobi / TENOR. / HAMBURGI, / Ex Officina Typographica PAULI LANGI / sumptibus autoris. / ANNO M. DC. XXII.

CANTIONES / VARIAE / V. VI. VII. IXX. X. XII. XVI. XX. / Vocum / QUAE SUNT / OPERUM MUSICORUM / Tomus Quartus / Cui in gratiam Musicae peritorum additum habes / BASSUM CONTINUUM / Divinae majestatis honori / Reipublicae Christianiae [sic] & Musicae / BONO / concinnatus & dedicatus / ab / HIERONYMO PRAETORIO Sen. / Organista ad D. Jacobi. / TENOR. / HAMBURGI / excusus ab HENRICO CARSTENS / sumptibus auctoris. / ANNO M DC XVIII.

CANTIONES NOVAE / OFFICIOSAE / V. VI. VII. VIII. X. ET / XV. VOC. / QUAE SUNT / OPERUM MUSI- / CORUM / TOMUS QUINTUS / Cui in gratiam Musicae peritorum additum habes / Bassum Continuum / Divinae Majestatis honori / Reipublicae Christianae & Musicae BONO / Concinnatus & dedicatus / Ab / HIERONYMO PRAETORIO SENIORE / ORGANISTA AD D. JACOBI. / TENOR. / CUM GRATIA ET PRIVILEGIO ELECT. SAXON. / HAMBURGI, / IMPENSIS MICHAELIS HERINGI. / ANNO M. D. CXXV.

The above-mentioned publications of Praetorius's motets contain few obvious errors and present no special problems for the transcriber. Instances in which I have deviated from a literal reading of the sources, not covered by my general remarks below, are cited among the paragraphs of critical notes that conclude this preface.

In the present edition, each voice part is preceded by a compact incipit showing the clef, key-signature, time-signature, and initial note as printed in the source. Throughout my transcriptions, Praetorius's original note-values have been halved in passages of duple meter and quartered in passages of triple meter. Mensuration signs are supplied unsystematically in the source. In passages of duple meter, C, ₵, and ⍉ are apparently interchangeable, and I have transcribed all such passages with the ordinary 4/4 time-signature. Similarly, in passages of triple meter the original signatures—3/2, C3/2, ₵3/2, 3, C3, and ₵3—have no discernible special meaning, and I have transcribed them all using the modern sign 3/4.[14] I have indicated the proportional relation between duple and triple meter by the signs ♩ = ♩. and ♩. = ♩ , placed above the top staff of the passages in question.

Notes bound in ligature in the source are designated in my edition by an overhead, horizontal bracket: ⌐‾‾‾⌐ ; colored notes, occurring only in passages of triple meter, are enclosed in broken brackets: ⌐ ⌐ .

Editorial accidentals are registered in the staff, adjacent to their notes, enclosed in square brackets; all accidentals in the staff, whether original or editorial, are good for the remainder of the measure in which they appear unless cancelled. Cautionary inflections have been indicated sparingly, in parentheses, usually to caution the performer against sounding an antecedent inflection appearing in the same measure in some voice part other than his own, or at the octave in his own part. The source uses a sharp sign to cancel a flat in the signature; I have replaced all such sharps with modern natural-signs.

The general clarity of textual underlay in the source is enhanced by Praetorius's prevailingly syllabic setting of his texts; occasional editorial deviations from the source's underlay, as well as instances of possible alternative underlay, are discussed in my paragraphed notes, below. Repetitions of text indicated by the abbreviation *ij* in the source are enclosed in angled brackets: ⟨ ⟩ ; editorial additions to the text are enclosed in square brackets; single words abbreviated in the source are written out without comment in my edition. The spelling and punctuation of all texts, haphazard in the source, have been made to conform with the *Liber usualis*.

Critical Notes

The editorial notes use the following abbreviations: I = the number of the chorus counting from the top of the score; the letter following a Roman numeral indicates the voice part (C = Cantus, A = Altus, T = Tenor, and B = Bassus); the number following a letter for the voice part indicates a first or second of that voice part, so that C2 = Cantus 2; and c. o. p. = ligature *cum opposita proprietate*. The Psalm numbers in parentheses are those of the King James Version. The volume and motet number of the original edition are given following the title.

Part I: Six Motets for Two Choirs

Ecce Dominus veniet (Vol. I, No. 1). The text to "lux magna" is the Antiphon with "Alleluia" for the

third Psalm at Vespers on the First Sunday in Advent (*LU*, 324). M. 15, IB: original text underlay reads ♪♪♩ ♩ ; m. 20, IB: upward tail to left omitted on ligature c. o. p.; mm. 51-52, IB: original text underlay reads ♪♪♩♩ ♩ ; mm. 55-57, IB: original text underlay reads ♪♪♪♪ ♩ ♩ ♩ ♪♪ ♩ ♩ ; m. 93, IIC: possible text repetition sign omitted under melisma "-ia"; m. 98, IIB: original has semiminims *g* on beat 4.

Nunc dimittis (Vol. I, No. 16). The text is the Canticle of Simeon, Luke 2:29-32 (*LU*, 1363-64). M. 12, IB: upward tail to left omitted on ligature c. o. p.; m. 40, IB: last note could be misread as *A* in the original; m. 77, IT: half-coloration, original reads ♮ ♪ ♪ ; m. 102, editorial 2/4 measure; m. 141, IIA: handwritten alternate ending added before beat 3 ▭▭ , and no text for alternate ending.

Cantate Domino (Vol. II, No. 4). The text is Psalm 95 (96):1-3 (*LU*, 387). M. 27, IA: original has ₵ preceding first note; mm. 47-49, IIB: original text underlay reads ♪ ♪♪♪♪ ♪♪♪ ♩ ♩ ♩ ; mm. 86-87, IIB: original has text repetition sign before "eius"; m. 109, IIB: original text reads "Canti:".

Ein Kindelein so löbelich (Vol. IV, No. 29). The first part of the text is stanza 1 of the German chorale which first appeared in *Enchiridion geistliche gesenge und Psalmen für die leyen* (Zwickau: H. Schönsperger, 1528). The text and tune used by Praetorius (more often set to the text *Der Tag der ist so freudenreich*) were first joined in Johann Spangenberg, *Zwölff Christliche Lobgesenge und Leissen* (Wittenberg: Georg Rhaw, 1545). The second part of the text is the Christmas carol *Joseph lieber, Joseph mein* which first appeared with music in Johann Walter, *Wittenbergisch deutsch Geistlich Gesangbüchlein* (Wittenberg: Georg Rhaws Erben, 1551). The original spelling of the text has been modernized. M. 5, IB: remainder of the text is indicated by "etc." to m. 77; m. 8, IIA: alternate text placement ♪♪♪ ♩ ; m. 83, IIA: original text reads "wiegen mein"; m. 105, IB: remainder of text is indicated by "etc." to m. 110; m. 130, IB: original text underlay reads ♪♪♪ ♩ ♩ ♩ ♩ ♩ ; mm. 143-44, IB: text underlay and added note were derived from a similar passage in IIB, m. 136-37.

Ecce quam bonum (Vol. V, No. 26). The text is Psalm 132 (133) found in (*LU*, 295). M. 1, IB: no mensuration sign in the original; m. 34, IIC: original has ♯ before *e'* meaning *e'-natural*; m. 37, same as preceding note; m. 41, IITl: original has a fusa rest; m. 46, editorial 2/4 measure; m. 65, IB: third note is *b'-flat* in the original; m. 68, IITl: original has

♮ before *e''* meaning *e''-natural*; m. 77, same as the preceding note.

Laudate Dominum (Vol. V, No. 28). The text is Psalm 116 (117) found in (*LU*, 166). M. 22, IB: original text underlay reads ♪♪♪♪ ♩ ♩ ♩ ; mm. 41, 48, editorial 2/4 measures; mm. 52-53, IB: text underlay is derived from I and from IIB, mm. 56-57.

Part II: Five Motets for Three Choirs

Jubilate Deo (Vol. I, No. 64). The text up to m. 60 is the Introit for the Third Sunday after Easter without "Alleluias" (*LU*, 821). From m. 61 the text is the Antiphon of the Introit for the Second Sunday after the Epiphany (*LU*, 484). Mm. 49-50, I: *LU*, 821 reads "tuae"; m. 55, IIIB: the first two notes are *e* and *d-sharp* in the original; mm. 64-65, I, II, and III: "Deus" omitted from text as in *LU*, 484; mm. 77-78, same as preceding note; m. 86, I, II, and III: "Altissime" omitted from text as in *LU*, 484.

Dixit Dominus (Vol. II, No. 6). The text is Psalm 109 (110) found in *LU*, 251. Mm. 56-57, IIIA: original rhythm reads ◦ ◦ ▬ ▭ ; m. 84, IIIB: original text reads ♩♩♩♩♩ ; m. 91, IIIT: original reads "bibit"; m. 96, IC: fifth note reads ⚷ in original; m. 100, IC: first note reads ⚶ in original; m. 104, IC: third note reads ♩ in original.

Angelus ad pastores ait (Vol. IV, No. 33). The text is an Antiphon at Lauds for the Nativity of Our Lord (*LU*, 397) with the addition of "Gloria in excelsis Deo, et in terra pax hominibus, bonae voluntatis" and verses from the Latin Christmas hymn *Puer natus in Bethlehem*. The earliest printed German source of this hymn is *Das Babst'sche Gesangbuch* (Leipzig, 1545), fol. Rii *verso* to Riii *verso* (see facsimile edition published by Bärenreiter in 1929 and 1966). Praetorius does not use the traditional tunes

for this text. M. 33, IT: natural sign is printed in the original; mm. 54, 61, and 68, all parts except IIC: cue indication "Pueri: Gloria in excelsis Deo"; m. 64, IB: "pax hominibus bonae voluntatis" is indicated by "etc." in the original; m. 77, editorial 2/4 measure, and IB: original rhythm reads ♩ ♩ ; m. 78, IIC: original lacks the meter signature; mm. 78 ff., IB: text underlay not clear in the original; mm. 85, 93, IA: second note is *g* in the original; m. 88, IB: notes are reversed in the original; mm. 93-95, IA: original text underlay reads ♩ ♩ ♩ ♩ ♪♪♩ .

Tota pulchra es (Vol. IV, No. 34). The text is a composite of phrases from the Song of Solomon 4:7, 11, and 10; 2:10; and 4:8. The opening phrase is an Antiphon at Second Vespers for the Immaculate Conception of the Blessed Virgin Mary (*LU*, 1320). Mm. 5-9, IB: text underlay is not precise in the original, but compare IIB, mm. 9-13; m. 24, IIC: first note is *e''* in the original, and is changed to avoid parallel octaves; m. 80, IIIT: original reads ⬥ ⊤ .

Domine probasti me (Vol. V, No. 30). The text is Psalm 138 (139):1-5 (*LU*, 184-85). M. 13, IB: original reads "met" for "me et"; m. 15, IB: original reads "cognovosti"; m. 24, IIC: semibreve rest in the original; m. 28, IB: original has unnecessary semibreve rest preceding semiminim rest; m. 56, IIIC: slur is printed in the original; m. 63, IC1: second semiminim and tie added by hand to the original; IC2: second semiminim and "me" added by hand to the original; m. 101, IB: original reads ♩ ♩ ♪♪ ; m. 109, IC1: beat 4 of the original has been altered by hand from ♩♩♩♩ to ♪♪♪♪ ; m. 115, IIIT: original text underlay reads ♩ ♪♪♩♩ ⌂ ⌐ .

Frederick K. Gable
July, 1974   University of California, Riverside

Notes

[1] All biographical information is taken from Bruno Friedrich, *Der Vokalstil des Hieronymus Praetorius* (Hamburg, 1932), pp. 4-5. See also Lothar Hoffman-Erbrecht, "Praetorius," *Die Musik in Geschichte und Gegenwart* X (Kassel: Bärenreiter, 1962), cols. 1556-59.

[2] Printed in August W. Ambros, *Geschichte der Musik* (Leipzig: Leuckart, 1911), Vol. V, ed. Otto Kade, pp. 404-18.

[3] Printed in *ibid.*, pp. 465-522.

[4] Andreas Werckmeister, *Organum gruningense redivivum* (Quedlinburg & Aschersleben: G. E. Struntz, 1705), fol. B-B2.

[5] Eitner *Quellenlexikon* lists an earlier Hamburg edition of 1618 for volume V.

[6] See complete listing of contents in Vol. XXIII of *Denkmäler deutscher Tonkunst*, rev. ed. (Leipzig: Breitkopf & Härtel, 1958), x-xi.

[7] Library locations of MSS are listed in Lothar Hoffman-Erbrecht, "Praetorius," *Die Musik in Geschichte und Gegenwart* X (Kassel: Bärenreiter, 1962), col. 1557.

[8] Dates with superscript correspond to the listing in *Répertoire internationale des sources musicales*, Ser. B: *Recueils imprimés XVIe-XVIIe siècles I1: Liste chronologique*, ed. F. Lesure (Münich: G. Henle, 1960).

[9] These are published as Vol. IV of *Corpus of Early Keyboard Music* (American Institute of Musicology, 1963), edited by Clare G. Rayner.

[10] As transcribed in Bruno Friedrich, *Der Vokalstil des Hieronymus Praetorius*, p. 13 and translated in F. K. Gable, *The Polychoral Motets of Hieronymus Praetorius* I, p. 125. The account book is now in the Hamburg City Archives.

[11] Modern edition in F. K. Gable, *The Polychoral Motets of Hieronymus Praetorius* II, pp. 427-88.

[12] No. 12 of *Anthology of Music* (Cologne: Arno Volk, 1961).

[13] Six motets appear in Vol. XXIII of *Denkmäler deutscher Tonkunst*, ed. Hugo Leichtentritt (Leipzig: Breitkopf & Härtel, 1905; rev. ed., 1958); the other motet is *Te Deum Patrem ingenitum*, ed. F. K. Gable (Minneapolis: Augsburg Publishing House, 1969). Thirteen additional motets are accessible in Vol. II of Frederick K. Gable, *The Polychoral Motets of Hieronymus Praetorius*, Ph.D. dissertation (University of Iowa, 1966), UM order no. 67-2619.

[14] At the same point in the same motet one will sometimes find different mensuration signs in the various parts; this appears to support the common meaning of the signs.

CANTIONES

VARIAE

V. VI. VII. IIX. X. XII. XVI. XX.

Vocum

QVÆ SVNT

OPERUM MUSICORUM

Tomus Quartus

Cui in gratiam Muficæ peritorum additum habes

BASSUM CONTINUUM

Divinæ majeftatis honori

Reipublicæ Chriftianæ & Muficæ

BONO

concinnatus & dedicatus

ab

HIERONYMO PRÆTORIO Sen.

Organifta ad D. Jacobi.

OCTAVA VOX.

HAMBURGI

excufus ab HENRICO CARSTENS

fumptibus auctoris.

ANNO M DC XVIII.

Plate I. *Cantiones Variae* (1618): title page of the *octava vox* part-book.
(Courtesy, Music Library, University of California at Los Angeles)

XXXIII.

Plate II. *Cantiones Variae* (1618): first page of *Angelus ad pastores ait*.
(Courtesy, Music Library, University of California at Los Angeles)

SIX MOTETS FOR TWO CHOIRS

Ecce Dominus veniet

4

Al-

Nunc dimittis

18

29

Cantate Domino

48

Ein Kindelein so löbelich

-a, du süs-ser Je-su Christ, das du Mensch ge-bo-ren

-a, du süs-ser Je-su Christ, das du Mensch ge-bo-ren

-a, du süs-ser Je-su Christ, das du Mensch ge- -bo- ren

-a, du süs-ser Je-su Christ, das du Mensch ge- -bo-ren bist,

-a, du süs- ser Je-su Christ,

-a, du süs-ser Je-su Christ,

-a, du süs- ser Je-su Christ,

-a, du süs- ser Je-su Christ,

bist, be-hüt uns für der Höl-le,

bist, be-hüt uns für der Höl-

bist, be-hüt uns für der Höl-

be-hüt uns für der Höl-

das du Mensch ge-bo-ren bist, be-hüt uns für der Höl-

das du Mensch ge-bo-ren bist,

das du Mensch ge- -bo- ren bist,

das du Mensch ge- -bo-ren bist,

Ecce quam bonum

Laudate Dominum

DATE DUE